INSIDE MY MIND

Edited By Wendy Laws

First published in Great Britain in 2021 by:

 Young**Writers**® Est. 1991

Young Writers
Remus House
Coltsfoot Drive
Peterborough
PE2 9BF
Telephone: 01733 890066
Website: www.youngwriters.co.uk

Printed and bound in the UK by BookPrintingUK
Website: www.bookprintinguk.com
YB0489E

FOREWORD

*For Young Writers' latest competition This Is Me,
we asked primary school pupils to look inside
themselves, to think about what makes them unique,
and then write a poem about it! They rose to the
challenge magnificently and the result is this fantastic
collection of poems in a variety of poetic styles.*

*Here at Young Writers our aim is to encourage creativity
in children and to inspire a love of the written word, so
it's great to get such an amazing response, with some
absolutely fantastic poems. It's important for children to
focus on and celebrate themselves and this competition
allowed them to write freely and honestly, celebrating
what makes them great, expressing their hopes and
fears, or simply writing about their favourite things.
This Is Me gave them the power of words. The result
is a collection of inspirational and moving poems that
also showcase their creativity and writing ability.*

*I'd like to congratulate all the young poets
in this anthology, I hope this inspires them
to continue with their creative writing.*

CONTENTS

Harrison Antwi (7)	63	Terence Sutton (9)	103
Kiera Patel (7)	64		
Caleb Adu (7)	65	**Trafalgar School, Hilsea**	
Yeva Ganopolska (7)	66		
Isabelle Boylan (8)	67	Jack Johnson (11)	104
Matilda Alves	68	Jessica Harvey (11)	105
Louanna Thomas (7)	69	Zoey Coleman (11)	106
Hazel Parmak (7)	70	Isabelle Banister (12)	107
Thalias Broshtilov (7)	71	Ilias Papagiannis (11)	108
Callum Haslett (7)	72	James Legge (11)	109
Santino Phillips (7)	73	Mohadisa Hashimi (11)	110
Theo Latham (7)	74	Keegan Marne (11)	111
Amelia Reeves-Hutchins (7)	75	Kelsie Davies (11)	112
Laura Zaslona (7)	76	Owen Sleath (11)	113
Aila Wahla (7)	77	Gracie Walters (12)	114
Reuben Tooze (7)	78	Daisie Sturman (11)	115
Effah Korsah (7)	79	David Burov (11)	116
Nana-Nhyira Osei-Botwe (7)	80	Mark Hague (11)	117
		Ethan Rogers (11)	118
		Justin Kirkland (11)	119

Northiam Primary School, Northiam

		Daisy Wilson (11)	120
		Lola Bramble (11)	121
Ariana Keyani (10)	81	Tristan Rainbird (11)	122
Ysabella Everitt (9)	82	Mason Cooper (11)	123
Alannah Ross-Smith (9)	83	Abigail Palframan (11)	124
Stevie-May Wright (9)	84	Lotty McKenna (11)	125
Lacey King (10)	85	Harvey Kent (11)	126
Jerry McKinlay (10)	86		
Alexis-Mckenzie Pilkington (10)	87	**Ysgol Llywelyn, Rhyl**	
Charlie Clarke-Smith (10)	88		
Alfie-Lee Ramsden (10)	89	Daniel Magee (10)	127
Sydney Care (9)	90	Amira Dawson (10)	128
Ruby Miller-Barratt (10)	91	Aston Kearsley (10)	129
Jack Denham (10)	92	Liam Hamill Iles (10)	130
Phoebe Brunger (9)	93	Nevaeh Cooper (10)	131
Jessica Haver (10)	94	Amari Price (10)	132
Katie Dickson (10)	95	Mia Jones (10)	133
Ita Harkin (9)	96	Leah Chitty (10)	134
Ethan Sellwood (9)	97	Iona Hamlett (10)	135
Jacques Osborne	98	Sienna Burrows (10)	136
Oscar Miller-Barratt (9)	99	Lily Atkinson (10)	137
Rudi Harvey (11)	100	Oliver Carter (10)	138
Poppy Corcoran (9)	101	Lloyd Hogan (10)	139
Harry Pitman (10)	102	Kellen Rogers (10)	140

THE POEMS

Daniel's Boring School Day

In maths class, I have to learn algebra
But how am I going to learn when I am eating a chocolate bar?
However, in science, I want to eat food,
But my teacher says I am rude.
After science I have gym,
I don't know why because I am thin.
At my locker, I placed my books,
But better lock it before Bob the Robber looks.
Yay, it is finally recess and I have my snack,
But what will we do without a funny little prank?
It's an English lesson, the most boring subject,
How am I going to finish the loudly, roaring, tiger text?
Oh no! It's reading time,
Although I want to play with my slime.
Finally, heaven is here, which is lunchtime,
I have my box and I read to start to eat.

Arundhati Saha (10)
All Saints' CE (A) Primary School, Peterborough

A Princess Addicted To Noodles

T he best people in my life are my mama and papa

H aving a helpful hand is useful (me)

I am an inspirational sister and classmate

S afaa is the best sister ever and daughter (me) anyone could ask for

I love, love noodles, crisps and cucumber (my favourite)

S ome of my brothers are annoying (all three of them)

M y life is the best life and no one can compare to it

E xcitedly when I come back from school I jump into the pool.

Safaa Khan (10)

All Saints' CE (A) Primary School, Peterborough

Everything About Me

I like to cook and help my mum and dad.
I love to play and clean.
I like to dance and sing.
I like my teacher, she is cool.
I like to help my grandma when she needs it.
I like to help my sister and brother when they are sick.
I like to do maths.
I like to help my friends.
I like to help my best friend whenever she is sad.
I like to joke with people.
I like to do my homework.
I like to sleep.
I like to watch TV.
I like to go to school.

Yasmin Corte Real Furtado (10)

All Saints' CE (A) Primary School, Peterborough

All About Me!

Hello, my name is Zainab,
But for short it's Zain.
I adore Maggi Noodles,
I love to get paper and doodle.
I'm fond of lovely cows,
MHA is amazing.
I'm not as fast as a tiger,
But I can assure you I'm not a liar.
I don't like being in the spotlight.
It gives me a big shock
When I see a lonely lock.
I love Miraculous.
Life will be tough,
But I'll make it through, that was me,
Who are you?

Zainab Tariq (10)
All Saints' CE (A) Primary School, Peterborough

You Know Me!

This is me in my world.
I know you would like to hear the things that I like to do
So let's begin...
I love pets,
My favourite colour is purple,
I love to sleep so much,
I wish I could hibernate like a bear,
I like my teacher,
I love my family,
I love baking cake,
I really like to help other students
And do my own homework
And last but not least I love painting and drawing.
This is me!

Manha Asif (10)
All Saints' CE (A) Primary School, Peterborough

This Is Me

T his is me, a person who likes sport
H ello, I've been in an airport
I f you watch something I'd watch with popcorn
S o what if I can't ride a skateboard

I try to focus in lessons
S o, I'm not very good at cooking in the kitchen

M e and my friend play
E ven though school is long, it's still okay.

Salmaan Asaf (10)

All Saints' CE (A) Primary School, Peterborough

This Is Me

E xcellent
M agnificent
M arvellous
A stonishing
N ice

K ind
H appy
A mazing
L oves cats
I maginative
L oves cakes

I love *me*, can't you see?
I am great
I am caring
I am lovely
And I love doughnuts!

Be *you*, so I can see.

Emman Laila Khalil (10)
All Saints' CE (A) Primary School, Peterborough

My Hobbies

My hobbies are football, basketball, running and playing.
My favourite foods are sausages, fish, chips, chicken nuggets and cereal.
My dream in the future is to become a scientist because you try new things and you don't do the same thing every time because you learn new stuff.
When I'm really sad, I forget about what happened and I leave it and I move on.

Sufyan Asghar (10)
All Saints' CE (A) Primary School, Peterborough

My Name Is...

This is who I am!

My name is **H** abibah
A wesome means trying
B eing Brave is being fearless
I am incredible
The **B** est people never give up
A mazing is the best you can be
H elping is something that will make y
outstanding

And one more thing
You are the best!

Habibah Javed (10)
All Saints' CE (A) Primary School, Peterborough

This Is Me

I go to sleep,
What do I dream?
About me,
And my perfect body?

I am beautiful in any shape or form,
My personality might be kind of cold,
Yes, I am very bold.

I love my hair and my eyes,
It is not a surprise!

Everybody is beautiful,
Even if you feel different!
You're amazing!

Laura Montiero (10)
All Saints' CE (A) Primary School, Peterborough

This Is Me!

I look in the mirror
And what do I see?
I see the me
No one else can be.

I am happy with all of me,
Ears to hear with, eyes to see.
My personality, my skin colour, my shape,
All make up me from the inside and outside.

I am perfect the way I am
And so are you!
Never try to hide who you are.

Umme-Aimen Rasham (10)
All Saints' CE (A) Primary School, Peterborough

The Picture

C alming colours like flowers in a meadow
R elaxing while painting busy pictures
E ffort to finish my painting comes over me like shooting stars
A rising through my body like trapped air trying to escape
T aking my time like a turtle in a race
E xploding colour like neon colours.

Taliyah (10)
All Saints' CE (A) Primary School, Peterborough

I Love Books

A wesome, addicted to books, can't stop reading
R oald Dahl is my favourite
M y book collections, all sorts
A new book would be a blessing
A nd 'Diary of a Wimpy Kid' would be perfect
'D iary of a Wimpy Kid', awesome jokes and story.

Armaad Dean (10)
All Saints' CE (A) Primary School, Peterborough

Alisha

A rt is what I really like to do
L earning about new things every day
I n art lots of colours we may see
S tationary equipment is what we need in school
H istory is interesting to learn
A pples are my favourite fruit.

Alisha Bashir (10)
All Saints' CE (A) Primary School, Peterborough

All About Me

I like racing and I am fast but sometimes I come last.
I can ride something I like, it is a bike.
I like football but I always fall.
Today it's a new day, it's Thursday.
I can ride my scooter to the left and the right.

Muhammed Ali Aftaab (10)
All Saints' CE (A) Primary School, Peterborough

All About Me

I like to eat vegetables and fruit like bananas and mango.
I like to play games.
I like to do gardening, I grow strawberries.
I like to play circuits.
My favourite game is Minecraft.
I eat pizza once a week.

Suleman Hassan (10)
All Saints' CE (A) Primary School, Peterborough

Aryaan

A ryaan is my name
R eading four times a week
Y ou know I play cricket
A football is what I play with
A nd I play tennis too
N ot a quick eater.

Aryaan Hussain (11)

All Saints' CE (A) Primary School, Peterborough

Who Am I?

A kennings poem

Epic-gamer
Daring-explorer
World-imaginer
Nature-adorer
Pokémon-master
Minecraft-builder
Roblox-experiencer
Rocket League-racer
Covid-survivor!

Zane Lodhi (10)
All Saints' CE (A) Primary School, Peterborough

All About Me

I like playing football and cricket,
I play with my dad and my brother.
We play on the Xbox.
My brother plays on the Nintendo Switch
And sometimes my dad plays.

Daanish Taiyab (10)
All Saints' CE (A) Primary School, Peterborough

I Am Nylah

N atural curly hair
Y outhful and smart
L ook beautiful inside and out
A rtistic every day
H appy every day.

Nylah Akintomide (10)
All Saints' CE (A) Primary School, Peterborough

The Ocean

The ocean sails,
It's like a snail,
Slow but with a nice breeze,
People might freeze,
Some see a light,
It's very tight.

Khadija Basharat (10)
All Saints' CE (A) Primary School, Peterborough

About Me

L for learning very hard
A for an amazing effort
N for never giving up
A for a healthy life.

Lana Rahman (10)

All Saints' CE (A) Primary School, Peterborough

Ahmad

A mazing and amusing

H ardworking

M otivated to learn

A nd

D etermined to succeed.

Muhammad Warfan Ahmad (10)

All Saints' CE (A) Primary School, Peterborough

My Wild Soul!

I'm funny, I'm smart, I'm silly, I'm mean,
I'm a drama queen!

I'm an animal lover, the one to be.
When I'm happy I smile like the sun.

When I'm sad I throw up a storm
With tears like an angry cloud.

I ride my ponies like nothing ever matters.
We are like a wild herd and we fly like an eagle.

I've got blue eyes like a marble,
I've got golden hair that doesn't care with its wild
curls.

I have a soul like a lion,
Never to be seen.

This is me!

Lucy-Lou Waring (10)
Green Haworth CE Primary School, Green Haworth

How To Make A Matthew Cake

1. Get a tablespoon of silly.
2. Get a nugget meal from McDonald's.
3. Have phones and PCs in the room.
4. Add an ice cube.
5. Add cheese.
6. Put gravity falls on.
7. Put bread in.
8. Add cheesy garlic.
9. Add sweets.
10. Add a gallon of sugar.

After all of that, you will have a batch of Matthew muffins.
They contain gluten, sweets, sugar, cheese, garlic and bread.

Matthew Hayhurst (10)
Green Haworth CE Primary School, Green Haworth

I Am Who I Am

I am very kind.
I want to work with the autistic and blind.
I am very unique.
I love heights, I never freak.
Sometimes I act and dress funky
And I wish there was such a thing as a black and red monkey.
I am sporty, funny and when I get excited I ping,
Silly, creative and being loud is my thing.
I love having fun and I'm adventurous
And I would say I'm fearless.

Emmie Hulme (9)
Green Haworth CE Primary School, Green Haworth

I Am Me!

I'm smart, funny, thoughtful and curious at times.
I'm happy, silly, messy and can be very passionate at times.
I'm kind and friendly but bitter when I'm stressed!
My favourite animal is a turtle
And I hate the colour purple.
I don't have any pets,
My fifth favourite colour is red!
I am me and you'll never find anybody quite the same.

Sana Mohammed (9)
Green Haworth CE Primary School, Green Haworth

This Is Me!

I am fun,
I am kind and... silly!
My top goal is to be the world's best football
player!
I am dreamful and love to clean
And sleeping is my thing!
I am mindful to my friends.
I am happy most of the time!
I have a habit of... being quiet.
I have a dream of having a mansion and a green
Lamborghini,
The world's coolest football boots!

Cameron Worthington (8)
Green Haworth CE Primary School, Green Haworth

This Is Me And My Family

As kind
As my mind.
I like football,
I love it all.
My dream is to be a fantastic footballer,
Or it's all over!

I have a dog called Bobby
And he's thunderously fluffy.
I have two sisters and two brothers,
I have one father and one mother.

So this is me
And my lovely family.

Stefan-Blake Allison-Howard (9)
Green Haworth CE Primary School, Green Haworth

This Is Me

B eing happy is what I do
R eading makes me calm too
I love animals, some silky, some rough
E ven though lizards are quite tough
N ew birds' nests make me giggle
N oisy neighbours make me wriggle
E ggs of a duck taste quite good

This is me.

Brienne Whittaker (8)
Green Haworth CE Primary School, Green Haworth

All About Me!

My name is Mollie,
My nickname is Dolly.

I am sporty,
I am messy.

I hope to be a world champion
And go to HOYS.
I am nine years old,
My favourite colour is blue-violet.

I am adventurous,
I ride horses for Lancashire,
My best friend lives in Yorkshire.

Mollie Rose Roberts (9)
Green Haworth CE Primary School, Green Haworth

This Is Me!

I shine so bright, as bright as a star.
I love to look at brand new cars.
My chicken loves to nick.
It would probably like a picnic.
I am very smart.
My favourite dessert is a jam tart.
Science is my favourite subject,
I love working on different projects.
This is me!

Kai Foley (9)
Green Haworth CE Primary School, Green Haworth

This Is Me

T all and funny
H arrison is my name
I like football
S port is my thing

I like pizza and
S leep, zzzzz

M aths is my favourite
E nglish is okay!

Harrison Hannan (10)
Green Haworth CE Primary School, Green Haworth

Me!

How to bake Keeka cake!

1. Get a bar of chocolate.
2. Collect a spoon of happiness.
3. Add a pinch of sweetness.
4. Add some fun.
5. Get some sweets.
6. Get a lot of sugar.

This is me!

Keeka Bury (10)
Green Haworth CE Primary School, Green Haworth

Sinéad Is My Name

S inéad is my name
I like ice cream
N ature is beautiful
É nd all the mean things people do
A nything is possible
D ogs are my favourite animal.

Sinéad Duckett (11)

Green Haworth CE Primary School, Green Haworth

I Am A Pokémon Lover

I am a Pokémon lover.
I am a kitty lover.
I am very smart.
I am a cat lover.
I am a tiger lover.
I am a ride lover.
I am a sausage dog lover.
I am a wolf liker.

Oliver Junior (8)
Green Haworth CE Primary School, Green Haworth

My Cat And Me

I feed my cat.
I brush my cat.
I pet my cat.
My cat purrs at me.
I water my cat.
I clean my cat.
I play with my cat.
I love my cat
And he loves me too.

Jack Salt (10)
Green Haworth CE Primary School, Green Haworth

This Is Me!

T yler is my name

Y es, I like to game

L oser I am not

E veryone knows my name

R ound after round with my game.

Tyler South (10)
Green Haworth CE Primary School, Green Haworth

This Is Me!

To create me you will need...
A cup of kindness,
5 jugs of mischief,
3 pans of mates,
1 teaspoon of fun,
16 cups of happiness,
2 buckets of jelly beans, blackberry and strawberry only,
3 bars of soap,
7 years of age,
Now you need to pour in the bowl,
Mix with hot water,
Add the other jugs of mischief,
Now melt the jelly means with the strength and fun
Because if you miss that it will end up as sludge,
Pour all of the ingredients into a slow cooker,
Set it to high, wait 3 hours,
This is me!

Sam Dey (7)
Harris Primary Academy Kenley, Kenley

This Is Joey!

I am an animal lover,
A YouTuber,
A gamer,
A slushy slurper,
Sneaky as a shark,
As orange as terracotta,
As strong as a brick,
Compass user,
Foil boat maker,
Blue boy,
Leopard lover,
Peculiar pupil,
Chicken chomper,
Panda person,
Cheetah child,
Beetle boy,
Hedgehog head,
Pizza devourer,
Football watcher,
Kiwi lover,
Simple dimple superstar,

Poppet brain,
7-year-old owl,
As smart as an owl,
Garden guy,
Chocolate child,
Milkshake lover,
Football fan,
Jumper lover,
Loyal friend,
Book bee!
This is me!

Joey Oakes

Harris Primary Academy Kenley, Kenley

This Is Me

M y name is Mia

I 'm tremendously terrified of heights

A rt is my second favourite subject in school

H ave two annoying siblings

A funny, unique seven-year-old girl

R ed and grey tie is part of my school uniform

R ed is my fourth favourite colour

I love school because it's educational

S carlet is my older sister

O xygen is my favourite trampoline park ever

N oah is my younger sibling, I'm in the middle

This is me!

Mia Harrison (7)

Harris Primary Academy Kenley, Kenley

Me!

I am a history lover
And I am a times table superstar.
I love to eat sweets every day
And I love to hop around.
I play cricket and play around.
I hang out with my bunny
And I cuddle with it all day.
So that means that I am a bunny lover too.
I care a lot and I am very kind.
I am also helpful.
I always help my friends
And I always play with them.
I like them all and they will be my friends forever.
You all are my friends.
They are all so helpful and caring
And they always play with me.

Vamika Ballaya (7)
Harris Primary Academy Kenley, Kenley

This Is Me!

I am a... bookworm, pet lover,
Summer wisher, times tables superstar,
Helping hand for my friend,
Park player,
Biscuit muncher,
Chocolate eater,
Loving and caring,
Helping out my family,
Making chocolate milkshakes,
Making my favourite chocolate cupcakes,
Love doughnuts for my mum and dad,
My favourite thing is chocolate cake to make,
I help my nanny bake,
My favourite colour is red,
Making my day is singing my favourite song,
It's the most important thing in my life.

Bo McDonald (7)
Harris Primary Academy Kenley, Kenley

This Is Me!

To create me you will need...
A sprinkle of stardust,
A pro-gamer, some blood, a clever owl,
A superstar Just Dance!
A doughnut and chocolate eater,
A sporty lover,
A loving mother,
A sprinkle of doggy love,
An animal lover,
Also a good reader,
A pro at netball and basketball,
A cup of kindness and happiness.
Now you need to...
Mix it, whisk it.
The secret ingredients are love and s'mores!
Mix again, pour it in a bowl.
Here I am, this is me!

Sophia Baillieu (7)

Harris Primary Academy Kenley, Kenley

This Is Me

I like emerald, shiny, tasty green tea!
I also like, actually love, cats and dogs
And body facts, school games,
VRs and my aunt's house as it has... two cats.
I also love my cousin who has yellow hair,
That's it for my cousin for now.
I also love sweets and I love my family,
Including Ace and Giulian very much.
I like art, drawing and I also get very inspired in games.
I also like spaghetti with ketchup.
That's it for now, see you later!

Joseph Abeduh (7)
Harris Primary Academy Kenley, Kenley

About Me!

To create me you will need...
½ tablespoon of annoyance,
5 bowls of kindness,
10 jugs of laughter and fun,
1 glass of sparkles,
1 box of a lovely voice,
10 jugs of skinniness and tallness.
Now you need to...
Grab a bowl, mix in the annoyance,
The kindness and the laughter with the fun.
Add in the sparkles, the lovely voice,
The skinniness and tallness.
Mix it all up and put it in the bed.
Once it's warm, voila!

Eliza Woods (7)
Harris Primary Academy Kenley, Kenley

Leonardo Di Maria

L iverpool fan
E nergetic
O n the hook
N ever hurt
A football keeper, the best
R unning down the wing
D oing the best
O h love to play football

D oing the best that I can
I 'm so good

M uncher of fish and chips
A rsenal hater
R unning at Anfield
I nvisible
A nd that's me!

Leonardo Di Maria (7)
Harris Primary Academy Kenley, Kenley

This Is Me!

A game is my favourite,
A car colour I like is blue,
I am a good helper,
I like staying on holiday,
I am a book reader,
I like summer wishes,
A movie is my favourite in summer,
A choc cookie I like,
I love my school the best,
I love football and soccer,
I am a light sleeper,
Candyfloss I like from a fair,
I like a tennis watcher,
I like to go to Legoland and Disneyland.

Mohid Haider (7)
Harris Primary Academy Kenley, Kenley

This Is Me!

To create me you will need...
8 cups of loveliness,
2 cups of happiness,
4 cups of annoying people,
6 cups of mischief,
1 cup of kindness,
A sprinkle of fun,
Now you need to mix,
You will need love and kindness,
You will need happiness and a spoon,
But the special ingredients are...
Smores and marshmallows.
You will need incredible
And you will need cheek.

Lola-Ray Thomas (7)
Harris Primary Academy Kenley, Kenley

This Is Me!

I ntelligent in art
S pecial in every way
A ctive every day
B eautiful and kind
E nthusiastic in English
L ovely golden hair
L ove dancing the samba
A mazing gymnastic routines

T ennis player
A rty
Y oung but brave
L oves crosswords
O utstanding
R ights for girls.

Isabella Taylor (8)

Harris Primary Academy Kenley, Kenley

This Is Me!

To create me you will need...
2 cups of kindness,
4 jugs of times tables,
8 teaspoons of happiness,
10 cups of spaghetti,
22 jugs of caring,
24 teaspoons of fish and chips,
26 tablespoons of pizza,
28 tablespoons of pasta,
30 packs of marshmallow chocolate,
32 tablespoons of fun,
Mix in a bowl and enjoy,
Cut it up and eat without delay.

Esmai Corless-Pinnock (7)

Harris Primary Academy Kenley, Kenley

This Is Me

S o loving to Mum
H air is brown
A mazing
R eally pretty
E xcited all the time
A m kind to people
H appy every day

G litter is my favourite
I am kind
T o help people if they're hurt
T o help cook
I eat sweets
N ice to people
S o nice.

Shareah Gittins (7)
Harris Primary Academy Kenley, Kenley

This Is Me

B eau loves devices
E choes
A wesome person
U nique

A mazing
L exi's my friend on Roblox
E asy history lessons
X -Men are superheroes
A n awesome man
N icola is my mum
D ino nuggets
E cho location
R ehmaan my friend is sometimes funny!

Beau Patrick (7)

Harris Primary Academy Kenley, Kenley

Me!

Y ou will need times tables practice

U nhappy baby and need to be a Muslim

S uper striker at football and has a dinosaur bed

U nusually found a dinosaur bone in the garden

F inally, never lost at football. Loves Kaiju from Godzilla.

A lso has 20,000 bucks and 1,000,000 Roblox.

Add all of you have me!

Yusuf Aslam (7)

Harris Primary Academy Kenley, Kenley

This Is Me

J oyful all the time
O h, I love playing with my brother
S ometimes I like building Lego
E very day I try my best
P ractically wandering to the next day of fun
H appy most of the day
I have a four-year-old brother
N othing I love more than my family
E ager to do all these things!

Josephine Tempest (7)
Harris Primary Academy Kenley, Kenley

This Is Me!

To create me you need...
A full-size football pitch,
A glass of brilliant friends,
A brilliant book,
A family,
A sprinkle of happiness.
Now you need to...
Add a full Chelsea kit,
Mix some character films,
Cook some games,
Chinese food,
Delicious pizza,
Some hummus,
Some speedy legs.
This is me.

Pawel Chilinski (7)
Harris Primary Academy Kenley, Kenley

This Is Me!

I am a swimmer and an animal lover,
I am as silly as a monkey,
I am a chocolate lover,
I am a lover of chicken and spicy rice,
I am as fast as a cheetah,
I am loving and caring,
I am a Liverpool fan,
I have curly hair,
I have brown eyes,
My favourite colour is baby pink,
My best friend is Esmai.
This is me!

Isabella Abena Jean Addison (7)

Harris Primary Academy Kenley, Kenley

This Is Me

I am a programmer and an amazing helper.
To make me you need...
A piece of happiness,
A piece of heart,
A happy smile,
Create a hard number sentence.
Now you need to...
Add lots of fun and happiness,
Mix it with a piece of good heart,
You will need a puppy to shake its tongue,
Mix it all up - this is me!

Arthur Tennant (7)

Harris Primary Academy Kenley, Kenley

This Is Me

F ootball is the best
A Crystal Palace shirt is cool
I like Chelsea and Crystal Palace
Z aha in football is good
A pair of Crystal Palace shorts is also cool
A pair of Crystal Palace socks are cool
N ever won against Liverpool.

Faizaan Ud-Din (7)
Harris Primary Academy Kenley, Kenley

This Is Me!

A tablet full of games,
A middle-sized rugby pitch,
A dash of enjoyable holidays,
A mix of sweets,
A movie cinema,
A maximum of presents,
A pinch of lots of friends,
A class of people to talk to,
A ten-week holiday or more,
A big Lego box full of pieces.

Christiaan Hanekom (7)

Harris Primary Academy Kenley, Kenley

This Is Me!

S uper stunning
I am the super stunning girl in the family
E xtra beauty
N oodle and BTS lover
N ever underestimate me
A lways shining and trying my best

M oney
A kind, loving friend
Y ippee!

Sienna Ashley (7)

Harris Primary Academy Kenley, Kenley

This Is Me!

H eroic like a hero

A m very successful and helpful

R eally love football

R eally love sports

I love ice cream on Saturday

S uper kind and helpful

O utstanding as ever in the world

N ice and brave!

Harrison Antwi (7)

Harris Primary Academy Kenley, Kenley

This Is Me!

K iera is kind
I am helpful
E aster is my favourite
R acing is fun
A bsolutely awesome

P retty black hair
A mazing face
T ime to do my learning
E ggs are nice
L oving.

Kiera Patel (7)

Harris Primary Academy Kenley, Kenley

This Is Me

C ool and fantastic
A ll must support Manchester United
L iverpool has Mo Salah
E njoy my cheesy pizza
B e like Caleb

A mazing Caleb
D etermined Caleb
U nique Caleb.

This is me.

Caleb Adu (7)
Harris Primary Academy Kenley, Kenley

Me

I am a...
Cat lover,
Ninja striker,
Candy stealer,
Mischief maker,
Green love,
Piano player,
Sometimes angry at Theo,
Pokémon lover,
Super striker,
Early riser,
Super gamer
And finally,
A good friend.

Yeva Ganopolska (7)
Harris Primary Academy Kenley, Kenley

All About Me!

I am an...

I ncredibly smart girl
S lushy drinker
A lways playing tennis
B ook lover
E ncouraging girl
L oving person
L eading superstar
E xplorer.

This is me!

Isabelle Boylan (8)
Harris Primary Academy Kenley, Kenley

This Is Me!

M atilda, the world's greatest person
A dmire myself and who I am
T imes table superstar
I ncredible girl
L uckiest person in the world
D oughnut eater
A nd I add joy to everyone's day.

Matilda Alves

Harris Primary Academy Kenley, Kenley

This Is Me!

L ouanna, I am a really funny friend
O utside and inside all day long
U p a level with kindness
A mazing friend
N ever leave my friend alone
N ice and kind
A m very successful and kind!

Louanna Thomas (7)
Harris Primary Academy Kenley, Kenley

This Is Me!

To create me you will need...
A full-size football pitch,
A pinch of humour.
Now you need to...
Add one piece of joy,
An elephant toy with a crash,
A good crash will make a splash,
A good laugh of a toy.
This is me!

Hazel Parmak (7)
Harris Primary Academy Kenley, Kenley

This Is Me

T he best food is cheesy pizza

H aving fun and joy

A good helper

L oves playing football

I ce cream is the best dessert

A Chelsea kit in my room

S o fun playing games.

Thalias Broshtilov (7)

Harris Primary Academy Kenley, Kenley

This Is Me!

C at lover and dog lover
A load of cheekiness
L ove of hanging upside down
L ike friends
U ltimate football player
M arvellous football striker.

This is me!

Callum Haslett (7)

Harris Primary Academy Kenley, Kenley

This Is Me

S uper striker at football

A pro at football

N ice runner

T he best goalkeeper

I ncluded in a football team

N ot a fizzy drink lover

O n a football journey.

Santino Phillips (7)

Harris Primary Academy Kenley, Kenley

Me!

T his is me, a clumsy, Slush Puppie slurper
H elping hand for all my loving friends
E veryone likes me and cares for me especially
Joey
O ctopus lover, for all my friends, this is me!

Theo Latham (7)

Harris Primary Academy Kenley, Kenley

This Is Me!

A melia, a good gymnast
M y favourite food is pizza
E xcellent at writing
L oves chocolate ice cream
I like being helpful
A mazing at doing my writing.

Amelia Reeves-Hutchins (7)
Harris Primary Academy Kenley, Kenley

This Is Me!

I am a...
Hamster lover,
Cheeky monkey,
Smart owl,
Chatterbox,
Fish and chip eater,
Basketball player,
Sweet eater,
Nature lover,
Funny person,
This is me!

Laura Zaslona (7)
Harris Primary Academy Kenley, Kenley

This Is Me!

I am a...
Helping sister,
Energetic girl,
Maths lover,
Cat friend,
Funny person,
Doing new things,
Being fast,
Chocolate eater,
Candy gobbler.

Aila Wahla (7)
Harris Primary Academy Kenley, Kenley

This Is Me

R unning master
E xcellent helper
U ltimate football player
B read and jam lover
E ating master
N ice boy.

Reuben Tooze (7)
Harris Primary Academy Kenley, Kenley

This Is Me

E xciting pro-gamer

F ruit lover

F ootball player and Liverpool fan

A wesome friend

H elpful and maths superstar.

Effah Korsah (7)

Harris Primary Academy Kenley, Kenley

This Is Me

N ormal and quiet
A mazing
N ever gives up
A mazing teacher.

Nana-Nhyira Osei-Botwe (7)
Harris Primary Academy Kenley, Kenley

This Is Who I Am!

I'm friendly to people who are kind,
I like basketball but I'm not the best,
I look quite ordinary but there's no one like me,
I love all animals, especially in the sea,
This is who I am.

I might be small but I'm certainly unique,
My favourite school subject is languages,
I've lived in seven houses and I'm only ten,
My dream is to swim with turtles,
This is who I am.

I have two fish, two dogs and a cat,
Half of my family are from Iran,
Most of the time I'm very loud,
Some day I hope to be a doctor,
This is who I am,
This is who I am,
This is who I am.

Ariana Keyani (10)
Northiam Primary School, Northiam

Me

Friendly with animals like Mother Nature,
Taller than the stars, who is this person?
Long chocolate brown hair,
This is me.
When I'm with a friend I'm quite attached,
Then protector forever,
Then enemy forever,
Great at drawing like Da Vinci,
Play the piano and I sound like the birds,
This is me.
I'm nothing special but certainly unique.
I don't fit in with the others but I glow in the dark.
Energetic like a cheetah, I like parks and football,
My smile is bright like a sun glimmering and
sparkling,
This is me.

Ysabella Everitt (9)
Northiam Primary School, Northiam

Me, Myself And I

This is me, I am wild, wild, yes wild, that is me,
Curious and quiet, this is me, curiosity comes for free,
Quiet I choose to be,
Bold, that's a good word to describe me,
I'm bold, bold, bold, this is me.

Bright, I'm the light in the dark, the one who guides a ship from sea,
Kind and helpful, passionate too, caring for me and caring for you,
All of these thoughts are in my head, like a scary monster under my bed.
This is me, I'm Alannah.

I am me and you are you,
We are all unique and that includes you!

Alannah Ross-Smith (9)
Northiam Primary School, Northiam

This Is Me!

I'm friendly to other people, I think about them
And I'm joyful.
I'm nothing special but certainly unique.
I'm loving to other people to make them smile.
I'm very realistic and good with animals.
Waiting at the bus stop for my brother,
People stare and it is creepy.
This is me!

Getting stuck in a tree higher than a powerline,
That definitely sounds like me.
I'm nothing special but certainly unique.
I'm passionate and courageous too.
This is me!

Stevie-May Wright (9)
Northiam Primary School, Northiam

Wild

I am very friendly to all my family,
I'm helpful to them when they're in need,
When I pull myself together I am very bold
And if I concentrate I can be really smart.

When I'm curious I'm more like myself,
I use my imagination to be very wild,
Yes wild, wild, wild, wild,
I have a very sparkling personality,
That all of my friends love,
But I'm nothing special,
I'm just unique and very wild,
Yes wild, wild, wild, wild.

Lacey King (10)
Northiam Primary School, Northiam

I Would Be A Snake

If I were an animal
I'd be a snake.
I keep my things to myself,
I like sitting in the shade
But when a game comes to offer,
I can't resist.
I run, I spring, I sprint, I jump,
I play and play till the bell is rung.
If I were an animal,
I'd be a snake.
I'm smart and clever, yes that's me,
I'm daring, I'm wild, a bit crazy too.
People say I'm weird, I'm not to me.
Yes a snake, that's what I'd be!

Jerry McKinlay (10)
Northiam Primary School, Northiam

This Is Me!

Stubborn I choose to be,
I'm friendly at times,
The punishment of truth is less than a lie,
I'm nothing special but certainly unique.

Forgiveness can be a real difficulty,
Just like controlling my anxiety,
curiosity is something that comes for free,
I'm nothing special but certainly unique.

I'm passionate to those who care,
Although helpfulness comes and goes,
I'm nothing special but certainly unique.

Alexis-Mckenzie Pilkington (10)
Northiam Primary School, Northiam

Friendly

I'm friendly to those who smile,
Girls in the corridor staring as I pass,
Don't they know how much I am loved at home?

I'm friendly to those who smile,
Waiting at the station, people stare as I pass,
Don't they know how much I am loved at home?

I'm friendly to those who smile,
At school, I'm being stared at,
Don't they know how much I am loved at home?

I am friendly to those who smile.

Charlie Clarke-Smith (10)
Northiam Primary School, Northiam

The Things I Do!

I'm polite to people
And passionate to my loved ones,
Helpful and friendly,
That's the thing I do.

I might be loud,
But that's what makes me curious,
Making people laugh,
That's the thing I do.

I'm not special,
But certainly unique,
Geography and football,
That's the thing I do.

The thing I do,
The thing I do,
The thing I do!

Alfie-Lee Ramsden (10)
Northiam Primary School, Northiam

This Is Me

I'm passionate, this is me,
Wild, but fun-loving to all pets and family,
This is me.
Silent but warm inside,
I'm nothing special but my family loves me.

This is me, bold, happy, courageous.
When I play with friends people come up to me
And say mean stuff to me
But do they know how much my family loves me?

This is me... courageous, brave and bold, created,
This is me!

Sydney Care (9)
Northiam Primary School, Northiam

I Am...

I am Ruby, this is me,
I have a life of curiosity,
I have two dogs, but that's not enough, I think I
would like more,
I have two cats as well!
I am Ruby, this is me,
I love my family.
My life is amazing, truly blossoming.
I am Ruby, this is me,
My life is perfect for me!
I love my life, it's like a light in the night,
I am Ruby, this is me
And I'm completely unique!

Ruby Miller-Barratt (10)
Northiam Primary School, Northiam

This Is Me!

My favourite animal is an axolotl,
I'm good at climbing trees
And helpful to those in need.
This is me!

Wild like a wolf hunting through the woods.
This is me!

Positive and passionate to all I know,
Courageous to them too.
This is me!

I'm good with woodwork
And great with a penknife.
This is me!

Jack Denham (10)
Northiam Primary School, Northiam

Me

I am funny, loving, kind and careful.
I love to help out and play with my friends.
I like to bake cakes especially chocolate ones,
I never forget to have the first one.
I love to play with animals
But I love my family most of all.
I play games mostly every day
But my favourite is hide-and-seek.
I am definitely unique, intelligent too.

Phoebe Brunger (9)
Northiam Primary School, Northiam

I Am Special

I'm not special,
Nor unique,
Lots of my friends
Call me friendly.

I'm not special,
But unique,
There is no one
Like me.

I'm not that special,
But really unique,
My favourite animals live in the sea.

I'm not special,
But people see me,
Because I am
Me, me, me!

Jessica Haver (10)
Northiam Primary School, Northiam

This Is Me!

I'm brave, I'm bold
I'm who I'm meant to be,
This is me,
I'm nothing special but definitely unique.
Who am I though?
I am a good climber because that is who I am,
I am a good friend to those who smile.
Does anyone know who I am?
People may think I'm useless but just wait,
You will see I am not!

Katie Dickson (10)
Northiam Primary School, Northiam

Helpful

Friends say I'm fun,
I love to help out,
I'm helpful and courageous,
Passionate and bold,
I'm loving to my family,
Also my pets,
This is me.
When people first meet me
They think I'm shy,
But little do they know I'm not inside,
This is me,
This is me,
This is me,
This is me.

Ita Harkin (9)
Northiam Primary School, Northiam

About Me

If I'm angry I can't calm myself down,
I am fun all the time,
I can be smart and work really hard,
If I'm lonely I can be happy by playing with my friends,
I am curious sometimes or all the time,
I am helpful to everyone,
I am loved by my family and my cousins,
I love to do running and walking in muddy woods.

Ethan Sellwood (9)

Northiam Primary School, Northiam

I Am Funny To Those Who Smile

I am funny to those who smile,
Thankful, forgiving as well.
I love being helpful to my mum and dad,
I am not special but certainly unique.
This is me!
I love playing games when I can,
I enjoy reading books,
I am funny to those who smile,
I am courageous, generous, passionate and considerate,
This is me!

Jacques Osborne
Northiam Primary School, Northiam

Me!

This is me,
Quiet, friendly,
I'm not free,
Can you go to the park with me?
This is me,
Quiet, friendly,
I'm not free,
Can you go on the slide with me?
This is me,
Quiet, kind
I'm not free.
Can you go to the shop with me?
With me,
With me,
With me.
This is me!

Oscar Miller-Barratt (9)
Northiam Primary School, Northiam

Who Am I?

I am someone, but who am I?
Is there something being hidden from me?
Do I have a disability?
In reality, I'm a speck of one of seven odd million.
Stuck in a tree, that sounds like me.

Some people think I'm not unique,
Get to know me,
I'm different than they think,
But who am I?

Rudi Harvey (11)
Northiam Primary School, Northiam

What I Choose To Be!

I am fun, friendly to friends,
This is who I am meant to be.
I'm bold too,
This is me!
Curious and quiet,
This is who I choose to be.
This is me!
When people first see me they think I'm shy.
I'm not when you get to know me.
This is me!

Poppy Corcoran (9)
Northiam Primary School, Northiam

This Is What I Do!

I like football,
I'm part of a good team,
Do you think I'm polite to my loved ones?
This is what I do.

I play proper games with my family,
Do you think I like the Xbox?
This is what I do,
What I do.

Harry Pitman (10)
Northiam Primary School, Northiam

About Me

I'm wild like a panther,
You're wild like me,
Other poems are not like mine.
I'm unique at school.
The girls outside the school are nagging at me
while moving out of the school.
I'm wild like a panther.

Terence Sutton (9)
Northiam Primary School, Northiam

Save The Earth!

Stop, we need to stop,
The Earth is dying,
Pollution, climate change,
It's all because of us.

The world we live in is slowly dying
Because of us, humans,
We are chopping the trees
And killing the bees,
It's on us!

But we can save Earth,
Recycle cardboard and paper,
Plant new trees and flowers,
Replenish the Earth.

Take some time to think about how to help,
Others have already started,
So why don't you give it a go?

Jack Johnson (11)
Trafalgar School, Hilsea

Me, Me

J udgemental, as I'm told
E ven though I'm moody I can be nice
S pontaneous with my words and movements
S ensible with them too
I ntelligent and independent, shame there is not
two, I is in my name
C reative with my words but chaotic with my
friends
A nd as you see I'm quite different with my words
and different from someone average, but that
makes me me.

Jessica Harvey (11)
Trafalgar School, Hilsea

Don't Let Go Of Your Dreams

Don't let go of your dreams,
Don't let anyone take it,
For one day
You will make it.

Don't let anyone steal your dreams,
Break all of the seams.
Don't fall into a great heap,
Take big leaps,
Don't let go of your dreams.

When you're feeling down in the dumps,
There will be lumps
Of confidence and courage,
Put it all in your luggage.

Zoey Coleman (11)
Trafalgar School, Hilsea

Passionate

P eople told me that I would never make it in life
A nd I would never achieve the grades I needed
S o I would believe them
S o then I fell
I continued to fall
O ver and over again
N egative comments were all I knew
A nd then I realised
T hat they were wrong
E verything made sense and I began to rise.

Isabelle Banister (12)
Trafalgar School, Hilsea

This Is Me!

I am from Greece, Italy, France and Germany,
This is all a part of me.
I live in the UK,
It's hard to live because the UK is trying to kick me out
And my family
And if that happens we have nowhere to go.
I love living here with my friends
And spending time at the library.
I enjoy exploring the UK.
I have two dogs,
Their names are Sky and Zeus.

Ilias Papagiannis (11)
Trafalgar School, Hilsea

It Doesn't Matter What They Say

No matter what you see
If you see dragons fly away
Unlike those dragons
Be courageous and stay

If you see things as easy
If you see things as hard
It only matters what you see
You could play music like a bard.

You can be what you want to be
You could even be a poet
It doesn't matter what they see
Your future isn't set.

James Legge (11)
Trafalgar School, Hilsea

Identity

Be amazed at who you are
Be proud of who you are
Don't hate yourself because of what other people
say.

Don't be shy
Don't say bye, say hi
To the world, you live in
They need you
More than I probably do.

Don't give up now
Look at how far you've gone
Think before choosing
Stay happy to win.

Mohadisa Hashimi (11)
Trafalgar School, Hilsea

This Is Me!

K eegan's very independent, also
E xtroverted and very organised
E xcept for when he's late like the other day
"G reat work for today," is what he likes to hear
"A nd don't forget the weekend is tomorrow," he says
"N ope," I won't forget.

Keegan Marne (11)
Trafalgar School, Hilsea

Picture Images

This is my image,
This is my worth,
It comes from the beauty
Of our wonderful Earth!

This is my image,
It is enough,
I feel that I am perfect
And if you don't like it tough!

This is your image
And you're special too.
Others may bring you down,
You will get through.

Kelsie Davies (11)
Trafalgar School, Hilsea

This Is Me!

O f course, he has a
W eird brain
E nergetic bones
N oble prizes, none he has

S tupid and smart
L etting others take part
E nthusiastic on his goal
A nnoying at times
T ough he is not but his
H eart is warm.

Owen Sleath (11)

Trafalgar School, Hilsea

Your Path

Don't follow the crowd
Don't listen to society
Don't copy everyone else.

What they do, doesn't matter
All that matters is you.

Make your own path
Follow your dreams
Follow your path.

The hardest path is the right path.

Gracie Walters (12)
Trafalgar School, Hilsea

How To Make Me!

How to make me...
3 scoops of sport,
500 litres of love of metal,
50 scoops of craziness,
2 litres of love of friends,
30 scoops of creativity,
20 pieces of good at singing
And now mix it all together,
Now you have me.

Daisie Sturman (11)
Trafalgar School, Hilsea

Delicate David

D elicate David can't handle a joke

A lthough he makes jokes himself he is

V ery inconsistent with everything he's done

I n the heat of the moment, he makes bad decisions

D avid's very delicate.

David Burov (11)

Trafalgar School, Hilsea

My Acrostic

M arvellously introverted

A dventurous

R esourceful

K arate obsessed

H appy for others

A viation fan

G ood at karate

U nderstanding

E ating.

Mark Hague (11)
Trafalgar School, Hilsea

Who Am I?

I am Ethan,
I have two dogs and one cat,
They don't like each other,
They fight, they run, they bark, they meow.
My sister doesn't like my brothers,
They like to mess around
And play football.

Ethan Rogers (11)
Trafalgar School, Hilsea

Images You See

Images you see are mountains, hills and houses.
The scenery you see,
The images are the things in colour.
Imagines can be black and white.
The money can be green,
But the cartoons are black and white.

Justin Kirkland (11)
Trafalgar School, Hilsea

The Daisy Poem

D esigning things is a hobby of mine
A mazing and bubbly personality
I ndependence comes naturally to me
S uperstitiousness runs in the family
Y is too hard for me, sorry.

Daisy Wilson (11)
Trafalgar School, Hilsea

Be Yourself

Let no one think that you are different,
Let no one tear you apart,
You are different.

Let no one say you are horrible,
Let no one steal your confidence,
You are perfect in every way.

Lola Bramble (11)
Trafalgar School, Hilsea

Hopes, Dreams And Ambitions

I really want to be a pro-skater
But to achieve that
I have to work harder.

I really want to be a pro-skater,
To succeed at it,
I need to work really hard on it.

Tristan Rainbird (11)
Trafalgar School, Hilsea

I Am...

M odest and ready

A imless but graceful

S ensitive but easily aggressed

O riginal but similar

N egative but helpful.

Mason Cooper (11)

Trafalgar School, Hilsea

Abigail

A verage

B ad

I nside

G irl

A person who has three brothers

I ndependent

L ong days.

Abigail Palframan (11)

Trafalgar School, Hilsea

I Am Lotty

L onely
O ptimistic
T alented
T ired
Y oung

I am clumsy,
I am annoying,
I am happy.

Lotty McKenna (11)
Trafalgar School, Hilsea

Harvey

H appy

A mazon

R eading

V ibrant

E nthusiastic

Y oung.

Harvey Kent (11)

Trafalgar School, Hilsea

This Is Me

I wake up and yawn as loud as a lion.
I go downstairs with my brother.
We fight with each other like cat and dog.
I hear my dad say, "Daniel, make your brother breakfast."
I go to school and hear the rules.
I just get on with it. "Okay," I say.
I go out for break. "Be good," they say.
I play with my friends, I run as fast as a cheetah.
I get told, "Do your work." I do it.
Finally, lunch, I sprint outside.
I have my lunch and come back.
I get told it's hometime.
I go home and hear, "How was your day?"
"Good," I say.
I go upstairs. Mum comes.
"Oh, he's asleep."

Daniel Magee (10)
Ysgol Llywelyn, Rhyl

This Is Me!

I love to dance, my favourite type is freestyle I think.
When I do group dances me and my team must be in sync.

I am very loud and have lots of confidence to show
But when I have to sing in front of people all of that can go.

I love Christmas, it's my favourite holiday
And when my parents say I can open my presents I shout hooray!

I like to go and ride my bike,
I also like a family hike.

I love Scotch eggs, the taste is the best,
I always ask for my mum to get some, she says I'm a pest.

These things make me as happy as can be,
This is... me.

Amira Dawson (10)
Ysgol Llywelyn, Rhyl

Game Or Swim?

I want to be a swimmer
I want to be a gamer
From when I get up
To when I go to sleep
I'm stuck in this situation.

I want to be a swimmer
I want to be a pro-gamer
I have some swimming goggles
And I have a gaming chair
I play Fortnite all day long.

I also swim all day long
At night I get some sleep
Ready to be stuck in this situation again
I have a pool
I have an Xbox.

I wish I could be both
But swimming is the best
So I'm going to practise holding my breath
underwater
For as long as possible every day I can.

Aston Kearsley (10)
Ysgol Llywelyn, Rhyl

This Is Me!

My favourite sport is football and I play it outside.
The weather doesn't matter, I will still play it with pride.

My favourite food is pizza, it's my favourite food to eat.
Pizza is so amazing, it can't be beaten.

I like to see my dad because I don't see him a lot,
Sometimes when I see him we play out at the park.

I like to play with my cat, he's really soft,
When he is hyper, it's hard for him to stop.

I like to go to school,
I think it's really cool.

These things make me as happy as can be,
This is... me.

Liam Hamill Iles (10)
Ysgol Llywelyn, Rhyl

My Point Of View

I've got a right lot of people in my house.
My sister is so little, she looks like a mouse!
When I'm in my room, I like to draw,
But when my dad goes to sleep, all he does is
snore.

I am sometimes angry, happy or sad
But when I am angry I sometimes end up doing
something bad.
I am sometimes moody, mean or cruel,
When I do that it's because I have to wake up early
to go to school.

I am very impatient, especially in queues,
When I fall over, I always end up having a bruise.
Me and my sister pretty much always fight,
But we mostly fight at night.

Nevaeh Cooper (10)
Ysgol Llywelyn, Rhyl

This Is Me!

My favourite sport is football and I play it if it is dry.
The weather doesn't matter, I'll still give it a try.

I like to learn fun new things.
I like to see the joy it brings.

I like to pick flowers to make daisy chains at play.
When the sun comes it soon fades away.

My favourite food is chocolate cake,
I like to eat it when it's just baked.

I like to bike on the prom with my family, it's lots of fun,
Together we have a chicken bun.

These things make me as happy as can be,
This is... me.

Amari Price (10)
Ysgol Llywelyn, Rhyl

This Is Me...

My legs are fast, I love to run
While I'm outside in the sun.

I love the subjects, art and maths,
I also love to have a laugh.

I like to play outside with friends
Making dens on a weekend.

My name is Mia,
I am 10, my favourite animal is a deer.

My favourite food is pasta bake,
I love to eat an ice cream with a flake.

I like to play football and get three goals,
then I go home for a sausage roll.

These things make me as happy as can be,
This is... me.

Mia Jones (10)
Ysgol Llywelyn, Rhyl

This Is Me

I love to go outside and ride all day
The horses love to come and play.

I love to draw, it relieves my stress,
I always hate having to clean the mess.

I like to listen to my favourite song,
It keeps my mind healthy and strong.

I enjoy being alone with animals outside,
Especially when I'm on a night ride.

My favourite food is chocolate bars.
My favourite ones are the ones called 'Mars'.

These things make me as happy as can be,
This is... me.

Leah Chitty (10)
Ysgol Llywelyn, Rhyl

This Is Me!

To make me you will need...
A dash of chilli con carne
2 tablespoons of kindness
A tablespoon of fun
A sprinkle of bossiness
A pinch of mischief
Now you will need to...
Add a splash of tallness
Mix in a chilli con carne
Stir strongly while adding
2 tablespoons of kindness
Next, add a tablespoon of fun
And a pinch of mischief
Spread the mixture all over a tray with baking
paper
Let it cook until it rises up
Sprinkle all the bossiness and let it cool
This is me.

Iona Hamlett (10)
Ysgol Llywelyn, Rhyl

The Middle Child

"Tidy your bed," Dad says.
"But Daisy hasn't tidied her bed."
"Clean your room," Dad says.
"But Daisy hasn't tidied her room."
"Pack your bag," Dad says.
"But Daisy hasn't packed her bag."
"Do your work," Mum says.
"But Daisy hasn't done her work."
"Do your chores," Mum and Dad say.
"But Daisy hasn't done her chores."
I have to do this because I'm the middle child.

Sienna Burrows (10)

Ysgol Llywelyn, Rhyl

This Is Me

My voice is powerful, I like to sing,
I like to sing about all different things.

I love to play tennis, it makes me happy,
My racket can be very tacky.

I like to wear something that stands out from the crowd,
Sometimes I can shout very loud.

My favourite food is sweet and sour,
I could eat it every hour!

I like to write stories and make people wonder,
Once I wrote a story about a hunter.

These things make me as happy as can be,
This is... me.

Lily Atkinson (10)
Ysgol Llywelyn, Rhyl

This Is Me

In football I love to kick the ball.
It goes over the free-kick wall.

I love to learn new things each day
Especially if it's the right way.

My favourite food is meat feast pizza,
I love it even more when it's made near the Tower of Pisa.

I like to take my dog for long walks,
I love him but I wish he talks.

I like to ride my bike,
In the countryside with my family is what I like.

These things make me as happy as can be,
This is... me.

Oliver Carter (10)
Ysgol Llywelyn, Rhyl

This Is Me

My arms are really strong, I love to play.
I would love to play outside all day.

My favourite food is pizza and chips,
I would like to eat it with some dips.

My dogs and cat like to chase each other.
They also chase me and my brother.

I like to do work in school,
It makes me happy, it's cool.

I like to buy new clothes,
Shorts and a T-shirt are my favourite things to buy.

These things make me as happy as can be,
This is... me.

Lloyd Hogan (10)
Ysgol Llywelyn, Rhyl

This Is Me

I like to play football and get a goal
And then go home and have a ham roll.

My favourite food is pasta bake,
I love to eat an ice cream with a flake.

Kellen is my name,
I like everything the same.

I love the subject math,
I love to have a laugh.

I love to ride my bike,
With my family is what I like.

Fortnite is what I play,
With my friends most of the day.

These things make me as happy as can be,
This is... me.

Kellen Rogers (10)
Ysgol Llywelyn, Rhyl

This Is Me

My favourite food is pepperoni pizza.
I love eating it in the Tower of Pisa.

I always make my friends laugh.
Sometimes my jokes could be a draft.

My legs are strong, from kicking a ball,
It is easy to kick when you are tall.

I like to play with my pets,
I felt happy from the day we met.

I like to go to school to learn.
I don't like school dinners when they burn.

These things make me as happy as can be,
This is... me.

Kyan Johnson (10)
Ysgol Llywelyn, Rhyl

This Is Me

My hands are heavy, they can hold a controller for hours.
They are so strong, they give me so many powers.

I love to play with my dogs.
We play a lot of fetch with logs.

I love to go to the beach,
When I touch the water it's so cold I screech.

My family is so kind and good,
All of us are understood.

I love fish and chips,
I get salt all over my lips.

These things make me as happy as can be,
This is... me.

Maisie Leonard (10)
Ysgol Llywelyn, Rhyl

How To Make Me

To create me you will need...
A dash of annoying humour,
A sprinkle of fun and kindness,
A blanket filled bedroom,
10lb of hunger and laziness,
A slab of hot cheesy pizza,
A spoonful of brightness.

Now you will need to...
Mix gently in a blanket filled bedroom,
Start mixing roughly while adding another slab of pizza,
Next, add a pinch of mischief,
After that put in a baking tray and in the oven,
Cook until glazed and filled as me!

Sophia O'Brien (10)
Ysgol Llywelyn, Rhyl

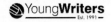

This Is Me

I am really small, I get bullied for it.
I walk or sit down to forget all of it.
I say to them, "Why do you bully me?"
I love my small body and my body loves me.

I love my family, they love me too,
My sisters and I fight like boxers but they annoy
me too.
My mum is kind-hearted, we all love her,
Everyone is important, not just us.

My hobbies are singing and dancing,
I've got lots of favourite songs.

This is me.

Charlie Jones (10)
Ysgol Llywelyn, Rhyl

This Is Me

I love football, my feet can kick with power.
It is so fast, like 100 miles per hour.

I love to do maths,
It takes me from the past.

I get happy when I am on my scooter
And I love my games on my computer.

Wearing my Man U top makes me proud,
When I go to matches it is very loud.

My favourite food is chicken bake
And also an ice cream with a flake.

These things make me as happy as can be,
This is... me.

Harry Brookes-Holland (11)
Ysgol Llywelyn, Rhyl

This Is Me

My favourite snack is melon
And when I eat it, it feels like I'm in heaven.

I like rounders, it's my favourite sport
And when I get out I still clap and support.

My favourite colour is pink,
It flashes in my eyes when I wink.

I have two guinea pigs, they like to eat hay,
Their names are Princess and Tiara and I hold
them every day.

These things make me as happy as can be,
This is... me.

Livvy Thomas (10)
Ysgol Llywelyn, Rhyl

All About Me

My name is Lily, I have nice brown hair.
I like to treat others with care
But I can't take a dare
Even if it is a scare.

I also like to game,
Gaming has been my thing until this day.
I play Minecraft, Roblox, a little Fortnite too,
All day long until the sun flew.

This is me, can't you see?
I'm as lovely as a honeybee.
I like to sing, dance and play,
All until the end of the day.

Lily Eccleston (10)
Ysgol Llywelyn, Rhyl

This Is Me

I do kickboxing so my legs are strong.
My favourite song is the 'Changes' song.

I love playing with my brother inside.
We do exercises and I am his guide.

I love to eat pizza, it is my favourite food,
But when it is finished I get in a mood.

My favourite holiday is Christmas Day with my family.
I like to open my presents.

These things make me as happy as can be,
This is... me.

Josh Williams (10)

Ysgol Llywelyn, Rhyl

All These Things Are Me

Loving, kind, caring
Water, swim, dive
Archery, range, arrow
All these things are me.

Sharing, compassionate, humility
Smart, enthusiastic, curious
Ready, responsible, respectful
All these things are me.

Happy, excited, calm
Embarrassed, bored, scared
Tired, thoughtful, grumpy
All these things are me.

All these things I enjoy
All these things are me.

Rose Kirkham (10)
Ysgol Llywelyn, Rhyl

This Is Me!

My favourite thing to do is read.
I finish the book at speed.

I like watching trains,
It's good for my brain.

I like playing on my games,
I have a Fortnite picture frame.

I like to pet my animals,
They are all sorts of mammals.

My favourite food is roast dinner,
It's a real winner.

These things make me as happy as can be,
This... is me.

Ellie Adderley (10), Mia Gregory, Joshua Thomas & McKenzie Ward
Ysgol Llywelyn, Rhyl

This Is Me!

My favourite food is pizza,
I like to eat it when I look at the Mona Lisa.

I have nice glasses
And long eyelashes.

I have two cats
And they both chase rats.

My favourite colour is blue,
Sometimes I like to eat stew.

I play on my Xbox with my brother,
I sometimes play with someone other.

These things make me as happy as can be,
This is... me.

Lilly Boateng (10)
Ysgol Llywelyn, Rhyl

This Is Me

I like school, it is very fun to learn new things.
I like the joy it brings.

I like to go outside.
I like to go on a bike ride.

I have a black cat.
She likes to sleep in a hat.

I live with my mum and dad
But I can make them very mad.

I love cotton candy.
The sugar can be very handy.

These things make me as happy as can be,
This is... me.

Olivia Pedley (10)
Ysgol Llywelyn, Rhyl

This Is Me

I'm a really good footballer.
I'm as fast as a cheetah.
I score lots of goals
And I'm angry like lions.

I'm as loud as a dinosaur.
My sister and I fight like dogs and cats.
I yawn as wide as a hippo
and I'm as clumsy as a hyena.

I am as nice as a kitten,
My hair sticks up like spikes.
Sometimes I think I live in a zoo,
How about you?

Jake Witherspoon (10)
Ysgol Llywelyn, Rhyl

This Is Me

To create me you will need...
10lb of walks with my dog
A slab of pepperoni pizza
A pinch of sass
A sprinkle of smartness
A dash of shyness
A tablespoon or four of clumsiness
Now you need to...
Add your walks
Then your pepperoni pizza
Now your pinch of sass
Add the dash of shyness
Add all of them tablespoons of clumsiness
And mix
This is me.

Addison Whittaker (10)

Ysgol Llywelyn, Rhyl

This Is Me

I can play football.
I can kick the ball against the wall.

My favourite food is chicken pizza.
I like to eat it by the tower in Pisa.

I like to work hard when having a laugh.
It makes it fun when learning math.

I love to learn and get things right.
I like to learn in different sites.

These things make me as happy as can be,
This is... me.

Thomas Baldwin (10)
Ysgol Llywelyn, Rhyl

Recipe Poem

To create me you will need...
A cupful of sarcasm,
A pot of funny,
A splash of mean,
A spoonful of bossiness,
A drizzle of responsible,
A box full of addicted to my phone,
A shot glass of fun,
The biggest glass in the world full of dumb,
A half cup of ADHD,
A bucket of not boring,
One shot of patience
And finally, a heart full of love for my family.

Lily-Rose Jackson (10)
Ysgol Llywelyn, Rhyl

This Is Me

To create me you'll need...
A cup of smart
A sprinkle of silly
A splash of good looks
A drop of dumb
A sparkle of short
First add a cup of smart, a sprinkle of silly
Mix to a good consistency then add...
A splash of good looks
A drop of dumb
A sparkle of short
Mix till a doughy consistency
Then bake for two minutes
You've then got me.

Oliver Jones (10)
Ysgol Llywelyn, Rhyl

This Is Me

T imes I'm reading
H iding in my room
I enjoy getting lost in a lovely book
S at in my own world without even moving a bone

I love myself and the way I look
S ometimes I say to myself, "I want to be a different way"

M ac 'n' cheese is my favourite
E ating it constantly, this is me!

Taylor Hoverd (10)

Ysgol Llywelyn, Rhyl

Chef Nihan... This Is Me!

C ooking is my favourite thing

H ilarious all the time

E ggs are my favourite thing to cook

F earless every time I use oil

N uts are the only thing I don't use

I 'm very talented

H oney is sweet

A nime pancakes are the last thing I cooked

N o cook is better than me!

Nihan Kurklu (10)
Ysgol Llywelyn, Rhyl

All About Me!

This is me, Emilia, I love to dance.
This is me, Emilia, I love to swim.
This is me, Emilia, I love to do handstands with my friends.
This is me, Emilia, I love to bake.

This is me, Emilia, happy and shy.
This is me, Emilia, kind and caring.
This is me, Emilia, adventurous and loud.
This is me, Emilia, and that's my life.

Emilia Roberts (10)
Ysgol Llywelyn, Rhyl

My Gaming Fun

There once was a boy called Andre
Who always loved playing his game
With his friends or not
He always had a good time
But he never liked peaking a lane.

Andre was never bored on his game
He really enjoyed playing with his friends
And when he was off it
He spoke with his family
When he was back he was ready to play.

Andre Stojkovski (10)
Ysgol Llywelyn, Rhyl

This Is Me

Hello, my name is Zara,
I like doing my mascara.
I am deputy head girl,
I love to spin around, to twirl and whirl,
My favourite dance teacher is Tara.

I like to eat bananas,
I love wearing my pyjamas.
My best friend forever is Chanelle,
I tried to do a backflip, I fell.
I hate it when there's drama.

Zara Monks (10)
Ysgol Llywelyn, Rhyl

This Is Me

To create me you will need...
A hamster-filled room
A sprinkle of kindness
20lb of craziness
A lot of fun
A dash of brightness.

Now you need to...
Add 20lb of craziness
A bedroom filled with hamsters
A lot of fun
Stir in a dash of brightness
Cook it and sprinkle on kindness.

Abbie Seabourne (10)
Ysgol Llywelyn, Rhyl

This Is Me

To create me you will need...
A bedroom full of pigs
A lot of craziness
20lb of mischief
A dash of fun
A sprinkle of happiness.

Now you need to...
Add 10lb of fun
A bedroom full of pigs
A lot of craziness
Stir a bit of mischief in
Cook it and add fun and happiness.

Ava Ellis (10)
Ysgol Llywelyn, Rhyl

This Is Me - Chanelle

This is me, Chanelle, I love to dance,
This is me, I love to sing,
This is me, I love to act,
This is me, I love to bake,
This is me, I love gymnastics.

This is me, Chanelle, I am kind,
This is me, I am thoughtful,
This is me, I am adventurous,
This is me, I am always me.

Chanelle Miller (10)
Ysgol Llywelyn, Rhyl

All About Me

I am sneaky and funny.
I like Godzilla and King Kong.
I like dinosaurs.
I am nice and silly.
I like pancakes.
I am crazy and kind.
I like pizza.
I am smart.
I don't like soup.
I like to play with my friends.
I like Fortnite.
I like Minecraft.

Kyeron Smith (10)
Ysgol Llywelyn, Rhyl

About Me

T all in size

H andy in doing work

I like playing football

S porty and fast

I like to play a lot of ping-pong

S wimming is one of my hobbies

M agnificent in life

E nthusiasm is my thing.

Lukas Stukonis (10)

Ysgol Llywelyn, Rhyl

About Me

What type of raps could there be?
Maybe one about me.
I'm kind,
I've got a really fast mind,
I never look behind,
I'm not fast
But I'm faster when I'm timed.
This rap will end in
1... 2... 3...
This was about me.

Danny Lavery (10)
Ysgol Llywelyn, Rhyl

This Is Me

Everyone's on their phone, it's crushing my bones,
It's like I'm sitting in a hot dome.
I am writing a poem
All alone with my ugly gnome
With a nice ice cream cone
But I'm not very known,
In that dome, there are shades of foam.

Logan Duffy (11)

Ysgol Llywelyn, Rhyl

Each Line Starts With This Word

I am fast, smart and sneaky,
I like to play with friends.
I am nice, kind and funny,
I like to set new trends.
I am a happy and caring person,
I am crazy and awesome Riley.
I am proud of who I am,
This is me.

Riley Radcliffe (10)
Ysgol Llywelyn, Rhyl

This Is Aiden

There once was a young boy called Aiden
Who lived in a bungalow in Rhuddlan.
He would dance all day
Until his legs didn't want to play
And then he sat down
And coloured the rest of his way.

Aiden Birch (10)
Ysgol Llywelyn, Rhyl

All About Me!

There is a young girl called Jasmine
Who lives in a bungalow in Rhyl.
I am ten years old.
My favourite colour is blue.
I am from Egypt but I live in Wales.
Art and cooking are my hobbies.

Jasmine Salem (10)
Ysgol Llywelyn, Rhyl

Gaming Life

Last week I lost a Fortnite game,
Oh, what a terrible shame!
So I got my friend called James,
He couldn't help me, that's a pain
And then I said, "The game is lame."

Leon Garner (10)
Ysgol Llywelyn, Rhyl

This Is Me

I am small, smart and sneaky.
I like to play with my friends.
I am nice, noisy and a bit nutty.
I don't like sausages.
I am crazy, kind Kailem.
This is me.

Kailem Griffiths (10)
Ysgol Llywelyn, Rhyl

This Is Me Football Poem

Football is the game for me
I love football, I play right wing
There's nothing better than football
I always want to play football
On every day of the week.

Ellis Birch (10)

Ysgol Llywelyn, Rhyl

Football Creates Me

There once was a boy called Lucas
Who was best mates with Puskas.
Football was his game
All he thought about was footy
And he had some custard.

Lucas Hannaby (10)

Ysgol Llywelyn, Rhyl

This Is Me And This Is My Poem

There's a girl named Amber,
She will play on her Xbox and game.
She will play with her friends
And sometimes beat her friends.

Amber-Louise Martin (10)

Ysgol Llywelyn, Rhyl

Gaming Kid

My name is George,
I love playing games,
I like the beach
And this is my speech.
When I'm done I go back to my game.

George Beggs (11)

Ysgol Llywelyn, Rhyl

YOUNG WRITERS INFORMATION

We hope you have enjoyed reading this book – and that you will continue to in the coming years.

If you're the parent or family member of an enthusiastic poet or story writer, do visit our website **www.youngwriters.co.uk/subscribe** and sign up to receive news, competitions, writing challenges and tips, activities and much, much more! There's lots to keep budding writers motivated!

If you would like to order further copies of this book, or any of our other titles, then please give us a call or order via your online account.

Young Writers
Remus House
Coltsfoot Drive
Peterborough
PE2 9BF
(01733) 890066
info@youngwriters.co.uk

Join in the conversation!
Tips, news, giveaways and much more!

 YoungWritersUK 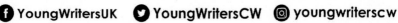 YoungWritersCW 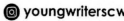 youngwriterscw